The First Rains

Story by Peter Bonnici
Pictures by Lisa Kopper

Macmillan/McGraw-Hill School Publishing Company
New York ▪ Chicago ▪ Columbus

Waiting for the first rains is a sticky business.
Arjuna felt it was like breathing with his head in a sponge.

The papers said the rains would come by the end of the week. Gopal said they would be late. "They can't be," Arjuna snapped and pushed Gopal to the ground. The air was electric.

Swarms of flies gathered everywhere.
The sugarcane juice stall was all of a hum.

Dark clouds blackened the sky and then moved on.
Arjuna thought they looked like warriors gathering in the
mountains waiting to storm down with all their force.

That afternoon, as he watched the clouds from under
a banyan tree, a kite shot out of the sky
and snatched his lunch from his hand.
"It must be a sign," he shouted.
"The birds are stocking up for the monsoons."

His mother was not impressed with his excuse for losing his lunch. She was busy sorting out the family's rainwear for the season.

The smell of canvas and rubber filled the room—it was sweet like rain.

In the streets too,
shopkeepers were busy making their
preparations. New waterproof awnings went up, stout ropes
lashed back anything that flapped, yellowing plastic
covered the sacks of rice. Even the beggar on the bridge
had covered his blanket with a plastic sheet.

On the day the papers had said it would rain, Arjuna wanted to wear his khaki mac with its pink rubber lining—just in case.

But his mother said, "Nonsense! The rains are going to be late this year." Just before leaving, however, Arjuna managed to sneak his shiny new rubber pumps into his satchel.

They all laughed at him in school when he put them on. And by the end of the day, when everyone had gone and the black clouds still gathered high above the banyan tree and the playground still blew dry and dusty, it seemed as if they might have been right after all.

Then, just as Arjuna was about to leave,
the light changed. The sky turned dark with
a strange yellowish glow. Street dogs
dashed around like mad things for cover. The wind
whipped paper and dust high into the sky. A deep,
dark rumble came from the belly of the clouds.

And then . . .

...and then
the sky burst open
and the rain thundered down.

There are some words in this story
that might be new to you. A *kite* is a kind of hawk.
Monsoons are seasonal winds that blow over the northern part
of the Indian Ocean. The southwesterly monsoon, which begins sometime in April,
brings very heavy rains to India, Bangladesh, Pakistan, and Arabia.
Mac is short for mackintosh, which is a raincoat.
A *pump* is a kind of shoe.

Text copyright © 1984 by Peter Bonnici.
Illustrations copyright © 1984 by Lisa Kopper.
All rights reserved.

Original edition published 1984 by Bell & Hyman Limited, London, England.

For reasons of copyright, this edition is not for sale in countries other than the
United States of America and in U.S. territories and possessions.

For information regarding permission, write to Carolrhoda Books, Inc., 241 First
Avenue North, Minneapolis, MN 55401.

This edition is reprinted by arrangement with Carolrhoda Books, Inc.

Macmillan/McGraw-Hill School Division
10 Union Square East
New York, New York 10003

Printed in the United States of America

ISBN 0-02-179486-3 / 2, L.7A

5 6 7 8 9 WES 99 98 97 96 95